DOT·TO·DOT
in Colour

WILDLIFE PARADISE

DOT·TO·DOT
in Colour

WILDLIFE
PARADISE

30 challenging designs to improve your mental agility

SHANE MADDEN

APPLE PRESS

First published in the UK in 2017 by
APPLE PRESS
74–77 White Lion Street
London N7 9PF
United Kingdom

www.quartoknows.com

This book was designed, conceived and produced by
Quantum Books Ltd
6 Blundell Street
London N7 9BH
United Kingdom

Publisher: Kerry Enzor
Managing Editor: Julia Shone
Senior Editor: Philippa Wilkinson
Editorial Assistant: Emma Harverson
Designer: Mike Lebihan
Production Manager: Zarni Win

ISBN 978-1-84543-672-8

2 4 6 8 10 9 7 5 3 1

QUMDDCA

Printed in China by RR Donnelley

Contents

Introducing Dot-to-Dot in Colour

Get ready to dive into a world of colour with the 30 vivid designs in this collection. Each of the dot-to-dot puzzles in this book has been inspired by the rich tones of the animal kingdom, from the sleek blues of jumping dolphins, to the iridescent shades of the tiny hummingbird and the resplendent hues of tropical tree frogs. Simply unravel the web of numbered points to reveal a stunning artwork. You'll be wowed every time.

Bringing Colour into your Day

Dot-to-dot puzzles are a great way to switch off from the distractions and stresses of our 24/7 world. Taking the time to concentrate on an absorbing task can help us achieve a state that positive psychology identifies as 'flow'. Flow activities enable us to tune out from our day-to-day concerns and become immersed in energised focus on the task we are completing. This taps into a central tenet of mindfulness, that is to say being fully involved in the present moment.

More than this, flow activities are characterised by positive channelling of attention and energy. Completing a challenging task gives us a mental boost and encourages a more positive, go-getting attitude. We can use flow activities to revitalise and refresh our minds, and gear ourselves towards a more proactive mind-set.

Use the 30 puzzles in this collection to set you up with a successful approach for the day, or wind-down with them in the evening. The dot-to-dots can be tackled in sections, or completed in a single sitting – simply fit them into your day to discover a sense of achievement and a calmer, more focused mind.

Join the Dots

Each of the puzzles in this book has over 400 numbered points to untangle. Once you get started, you will find the rhythm, following one point to the next to reveal a dynamic scene from the wildlife world. Before you get started, turn to page 10 for top tips on how to approach these extreme dot-to-dots.

Choose which puzzle to start with by turning to the Dot-to-Dot Index on pages 77–79. A thumbnail of each image will help you take your pick from regal jungle beasts, minute insect masterpieces and preening feathered friends. Creatures from all over the animal kingdom splash their colours across the pages and are perfect subjects for this lively dot-to-dot treatment. All of the pages are blank on the reverse side, which means you can remove and frame your work when you're done.

How to Use This Book

Before you dive into the colourful world of the dot-to-dots in this collection, read through the following pages for advice on how to use this book and for top tips on completing these fiendish puzzles.

A key for each puzzle shows the order in which the colour-coded sections should be completed. Follow this order to ensure no premature crossing out of numbers or dots in other sections. The key also lists how many numbered points there are in each section so you can easily identify when you have completed that colour. Read the colour order down each column, starting with the left column.

Each coloured section starts with number '1'. The first point is indicated by a star to identify the beginning for each line.

The reverse of each page has been left blank so that you can remove your finished puzzle and display if you wish. However, some reverse pages have colour keys. Check the back of each design before removing as you may need the key to complete the next puzzle in the book.

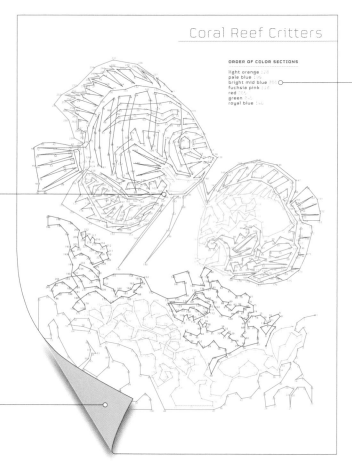

Coral Reef Critters

ORDER OF COLOR SECTIONS

light orange 1/8
pale blue 1/95
bright mid blue 201
fuchsia pink 118
red 175
green 7-3
royal blue 146

Match your colours to those listed in the key for each section. You have the freedom within each colour to decide your own tones or shades should you wish.

Turn to pages 77–79 to find finished thumbnails for each of the puzzles in this book. You can use this index to help select which scene from the animal kingdom you would like to try next, or if you need some guidance to complete the puzzle.

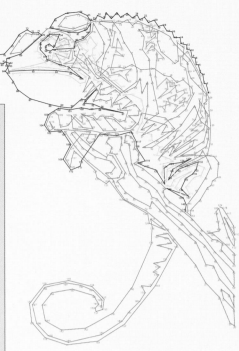

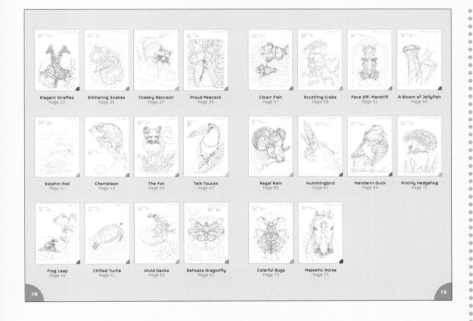

CHOOSING YOUR TOOLS

To complete the puzzles accurately, it is best to use a fine-nibbed felt-tip or roller ball pen in each of the colours listed in the key. You need to be able to keep your lines sharp and clear in those areas where the dots are close together. You can experiment with different types of pen, but we recommend using Staedler triplus fineliner, 0.3 mm, and Stabilo Point 88, fine 0.4 mm pens, both of which can be found online and in good craft shops.

The colours listed in the key provide a palette guideline. You have the freedom within each colour to decide your own tones or shades. You may wish to take some time testing your chosen pens on a spare sheet of paper before starting the puzzle.

Tackling the Dot-to-Dots

The illustrations in this book have been designed with vivid colour palettes to evoke the hues of the natural world. The coloured sections are worked in the main from lightest colour to darkest. Follow the order listed in the key to ensure the best result.

Each coloured section starts with number '1' and progresses chronologically to the end dot. The total number of dots in each section is listed in the key so you can identify when you have completed each section. It makes sense to join all of the dots in one section before progressing to the next, following the order recommended in the key.

Everyone will have their own method for approaching these fiendish puzzles, but below are some tips to help you get started.

1. **Prepare your tools:** We recommended using fine-nibbed pens (see Choosing your Tools, page 9) to complete the dot-to-dots, but you can also use coloured pencils. If choosing pencils, make sure that they are sharp before you begin so you can keep your lines fine in detailed areas.

2. **Get comfortable:** You can choose to complete these puzzles wherever you like – on your commute, in a lunch break or in a café. However, to get the most out of the puzzles it is best to choose a quiet spot where you will not be disturbed so that you can fully focus on the task in hand. Having a flat surface to work on with plenty of space will also help.

3. **Use a ruler:** Some of the points are quite far away from each other, and using a ruler will help to keep your lines sharp in more congested areas.

4. **Take it in order:** Each puzzle has been designed to be completed in a certain colour order as denoted by the accompanying key. Follow this order so as to avoid crossing through any numbers before you need to use them.

5. **Don't worry:** Try not to get frustrated if you go wrong. Simply locate the error and go back to the last correct point. You will still have a beautifully coloured puzzle when you finish.

6. **Closer look:** In some detailed areas you may wish to use a magnifying glass to help you read the numbers clearly.

7. **Pen bleed:** Each reverse side of the puzzle has been left blank so that you can remove your designs once completed, and also to protect against ink bleeding through the page. If you are concerned about your pens bleeding through the paper, simply place a sheet of A4 blank paper behind the puzzle that you are working on.

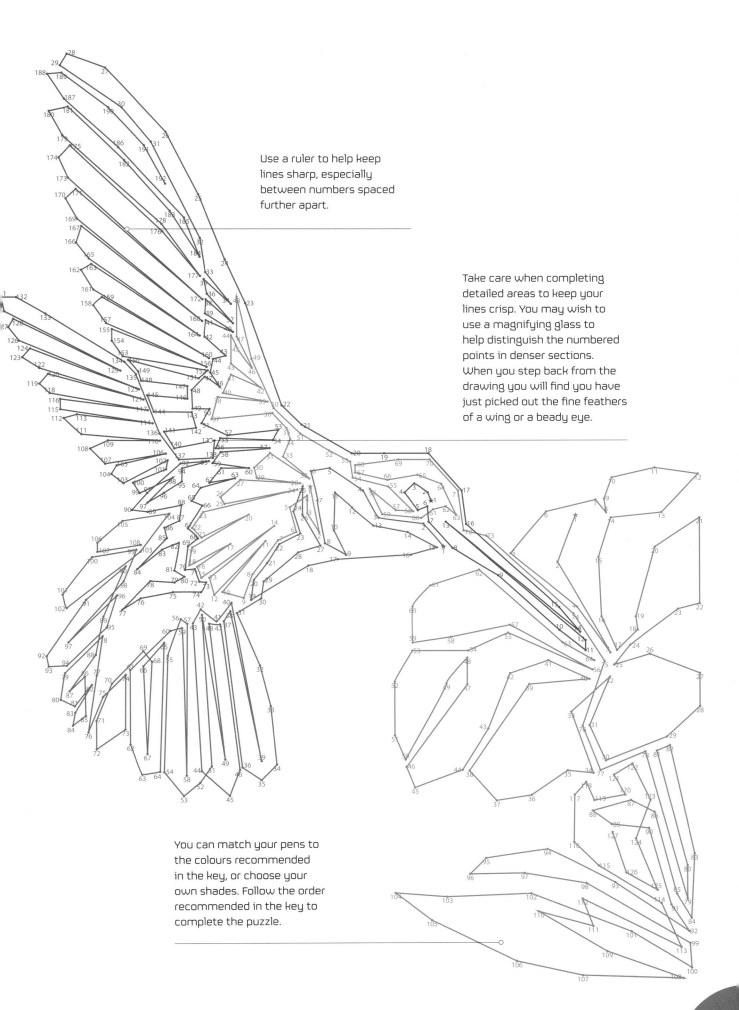

Use a ruler to help keep lines sharp, especially between numbers spaced further apart.

Take care when completing detailed areas to keep your lines crisp. You may wish to use a magnifying glass to help distinguish the numbered points in denser sections. When you step back from the drawing you will find you have just picked out the fine feathers of a wing or a beady eye.

You can match your pens to the colours recommended in the key, or choose your own shades. Follow the order recommended in the key to complete the puzzle.

Creating with Colour

Using colour has been made easy in this book, with expert colour-coded palettes developed for each image to bring the scene strikingly to life – and you can bring your own flair to each drawing by colouring in the completed puzzle.

Colouring Tools

While you need a sharp pencil or fine-nibbed pen to keep your lines crisp when completing the dot-to-dot puzzle, you can choose from a range of options to add colour to your image.

Coloured pencils are the tool of choice for most colouring in as they can be used to create subtle tonal variations within the image as well as adding fine details. Another option is **watercolour pencils**, which can create a lovely painterly effect; and for a bolder approach, **felt-tip pens** create rich, vibrant images with strong colour. You can also experiment with **pastels**, **paints** and **crayons** to realise a range of different styles. Have fun and explore the different artistic effects you create simply by changing your colouring tools!

Basic Shading Techniques

There are a number of different shading techniques that you can use to add colour to your dot-to-dot design, all of which create slightly different effects.

Hatching

Hatching is a series of lines drawn together to give a sense of filled colour. The hatching lines can be either straight or curved, and can be drawn close together to give a smooth effect or further apart for a more sketchy look. Hatching is a great way to add colour quickly to an image.

Cross-hatching

In cross-hatching one set of lines overlaps another set. Like hatching, cross-hatching can be drawn with the lines close together to create a solid effect or more spaced out with white spaces remaining. For areas of colour that you want to appear very smooth, close cross-hatching is the best method.

Circular shading

You can also shade with small circles rather than straight lines. Again, you can create denser or more roughly coloured areas depending on how close together you keep your lines. This method can be useful for creating texture within your image.

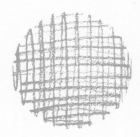

Drawing hatching lines close to and overlapping one another creates a smooth area of colour.

When drawn farther apart from one another the hatching lines remain distinct.

Cross-hatching when lines are drawn very close together can create a dense solid colour.

Spaced further apart, cross-hatching lines remain distinct and show areas of white space.

Adding Light and Shade

Create shape and bring depth to each design by adding areas of light and shade. Shading with coloured pencils or watercolour pencils is the easiest way to do this. The simplest method is pressure shading, where you place more or less pressure on your pencil to achieve a darker or lighter shade. Alternatively, shade the full area with the lightest shade then go back over areas that you want to make darker, adding extra layers of colour to achieve the desired effect.

Shading with pencils can leave flecks of white and show lines between more heavily and less shaded areas. To smooth out the colour in your image you can use a colourless blender pencil. Available from most good craft shops, blender pencils can be applied over the top of coloured pencils to better merge the different tones.

To intensify shading, you can layer darker colours over basic shading. Layering colours in this way will create a different shade from either of the original colours used and can make for an interesting tonal variation. You can also use different tones within a colour range to achieve more depth in your image.

Creating Shape

When adding light and shade to create shape in your image there are three key terms to remember: highlights, shadows and mid-tones. To create a sense of perspective you will want to add highlights to areas of the image that would be in the sun and shadow in those areas that would be facing away from the light source – mid-tones are those areas in between. You can use the shading techniques above to create these areas of light and shade within your dot-to-dot design.

THE
DOT-TO-DOT
PUZZLES

Dawn Chorus

ORDER OF COLOUR SECTIONS

orange 76

leaf green 93

light brown 79

coral pink 109

fuchsia pink 154

royal blue 100

burgundy red 98

black 104

Dylan

Coral Reef Critters

Coral Reef Critters

ORDER OF COLOUR SECTIONS

light orange 126
pale blue 199
bright mid blue 201
fuchsia pink 118
red 265
green 245
royal blue 146

Lion's Roar

ORDER OF COLOUR SECTIONS

golden brown 21
rich brown 540
black 187

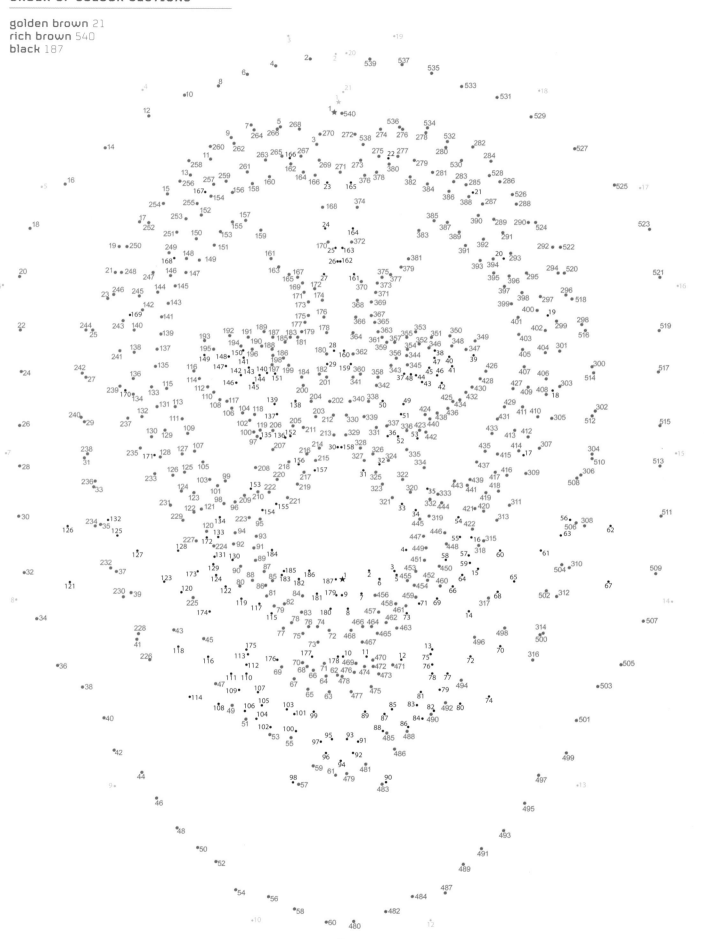

Macaws

ORDER OF COLOUR SECTIONS

light orange 112
bright blue 110
tangerine orange 148
bright red 104
light brown 79
forest green
upper leaf 147;
lower leaf 180;
black 190

Crowing Cockerel

ORDER OF COLOUR SECTIONS

golden yellow 83
orange 159
forest green 324
royal blue 35

bright red 63
burgundy red 50
dark brown 54

Flutter Butterfly

ORDER OF COLOUR SECTIONS

dusty pink 204　　light orange 18
duck egg blue 43　tangerine orange 68
green 121　　　　dark blue 296

Tiger Stripes

ORDER OF COLOUR SECTIONS

lime green 7
golden yellow 106
tangerine orange 214
warm grey 168
grass green 82
black 636

29

Flamingo Duo

ORDER OF COLOUR SECTIONS

pale peach 65
soft sea grey 64
azure sea blue 93
sea green 29
orange 8
tail feather peach 36

golden yellow 11
fuchsia pink 130
tail feather burgundy 81
pale pink brown 47
dark brown 70

Elegant Giraffes

Elegant Giraffes

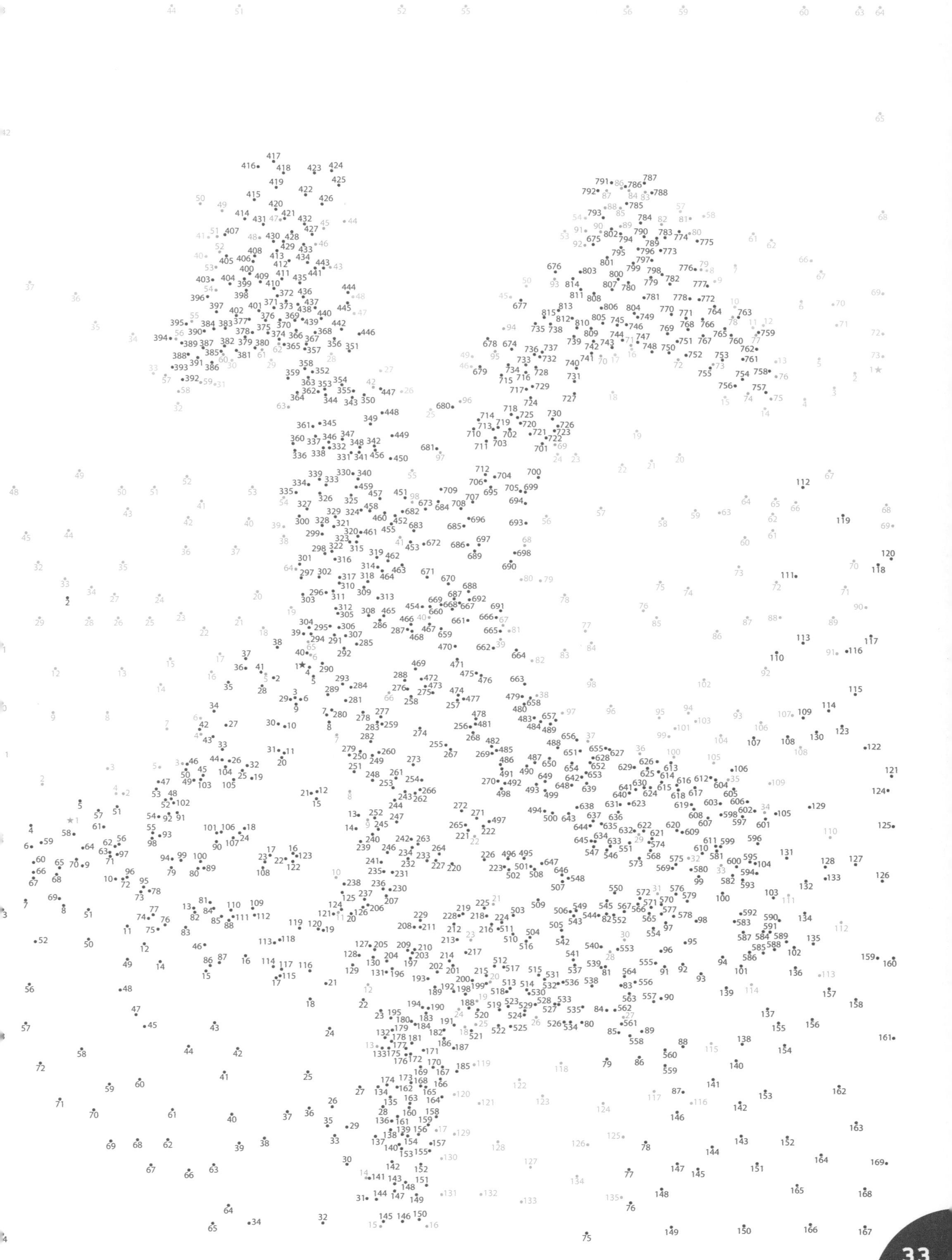

Slithering Snakes

ORDER OF COLOUR SECTIONS

pale orange 151   royal blue 263
grass green 288   violet 38
tangerine orange 218 black 43
fuchsia pink 209

Cheeky Raccoon

Cheeky Raccoon

ORDER OF COLOUR SECTIONS

warm grey 205
golden orange 219
brown 359
black 180

Proud Peacock

ORDER OF COLOUR SECTIONS

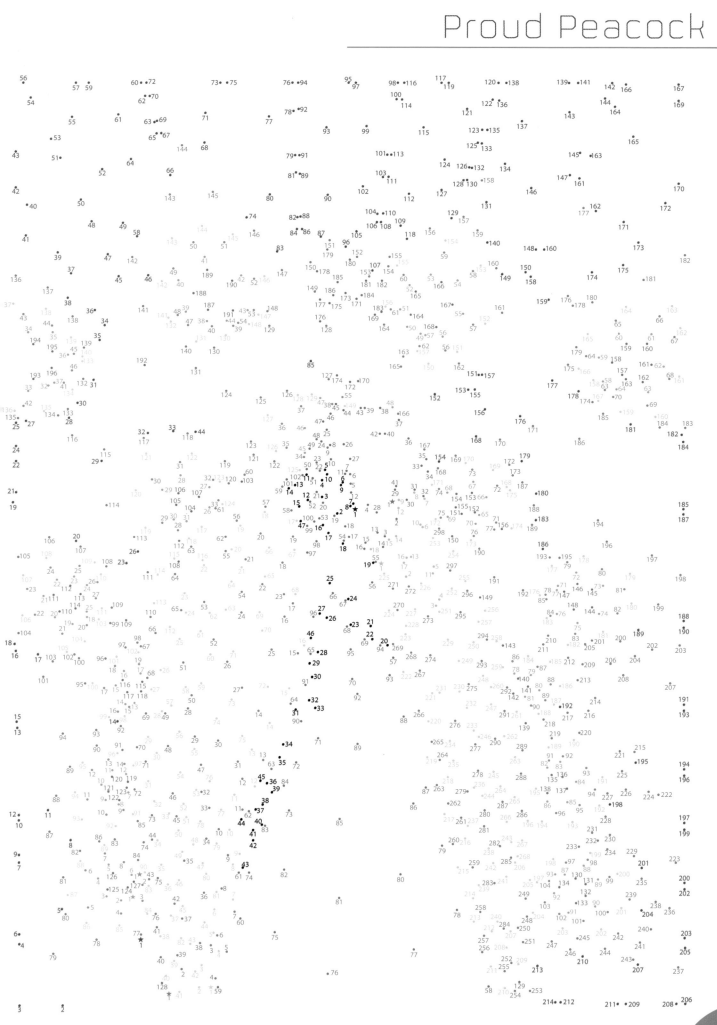

Dolphin Pod

ORDER OF COLOUR SECTIONS

golden yellow 130 royal sea blue 87
palest sea blue 55 grey dolphin blue 135
mid sea blue 94 navy dolphin blue 151

Chameleon

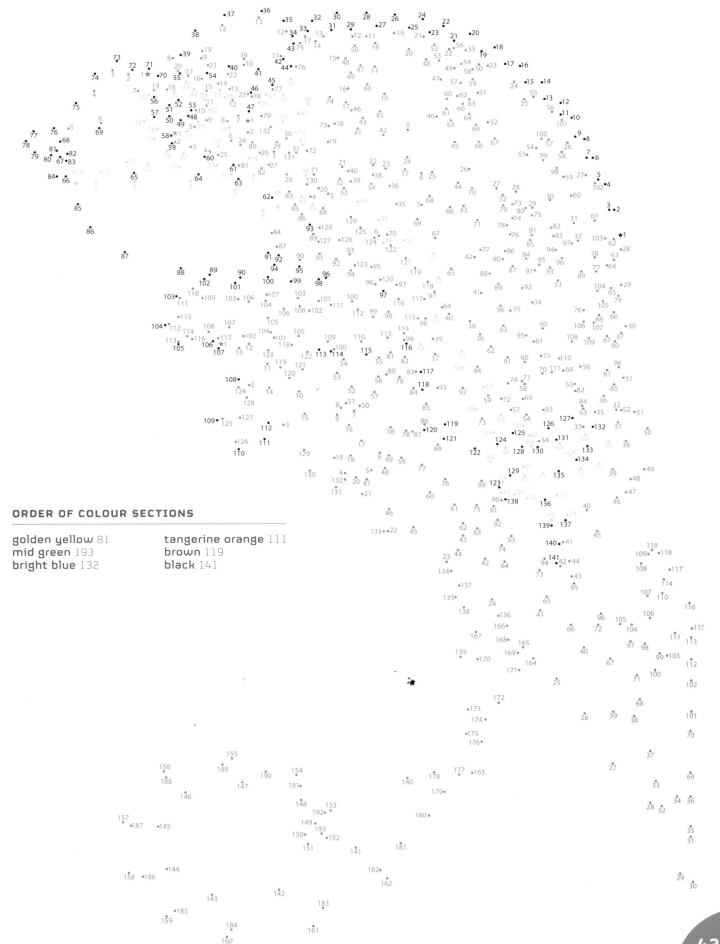

ORDER OF COLOUR SECTIONS

golden yellow 81
mid green 193
bright blue 132

tangerine orange 111
brown 119
black 141

The Fox

ORDER OF COLOUR SECTIONS

pale brown 237   grass green 142
mushroom brown 53   forest green 52
orange 263   black 196
bright blue 180

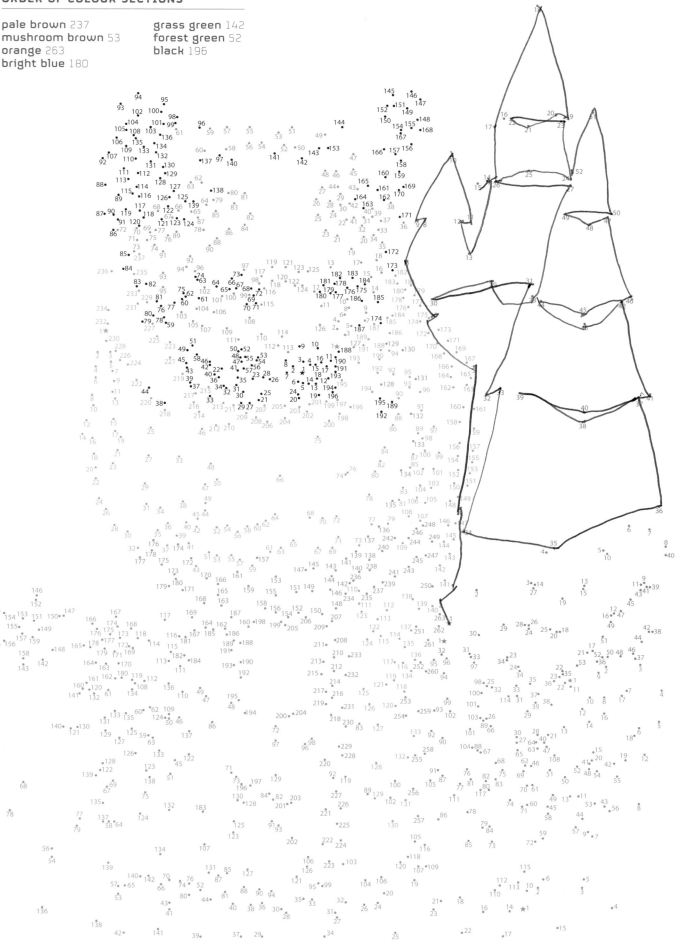

Talk Toucan

ORDER OF COLOUR SECTIONS

golden yellow 139
dark brown 92
light brown 53
leaf green 182
bright blue 24
fuchsia pink 46
red 56
black 226

Frog Leap

ORDER OF COLOUR SECTIONS

light orange 69
leaf green 239
forest green 142

royal blue 144
bright red 158
black 105

Chilled Turtle

Chilled Turtle

ORDER OF COLOUR SECTIONS

Vivid Gecko

ORDER OF COLOUR SECTIONS

light green 185
pale brown 191
forest green 254

bright red 103
black 20

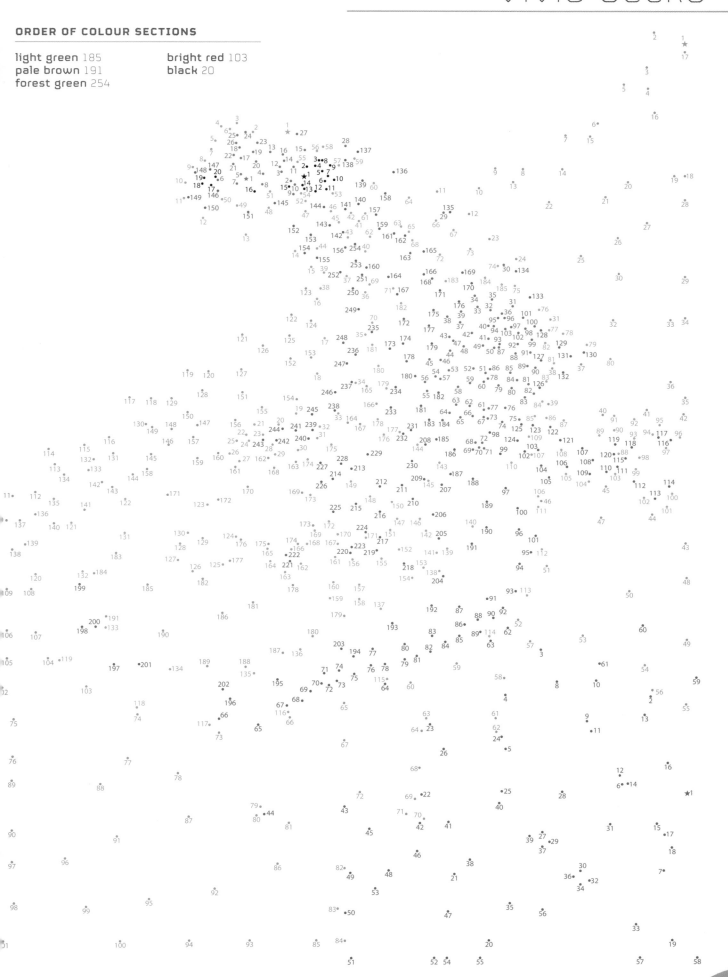

Delicate Dragonfly

ORDER OF COLOUR SECTIONS

golden yellow 65	royal purple 75
bright blue 115	dark green 166
fuchsia pink 364	royal blue 146

Clown Fish

Clown Fish

ORDER OF COLOUR SECTIONS

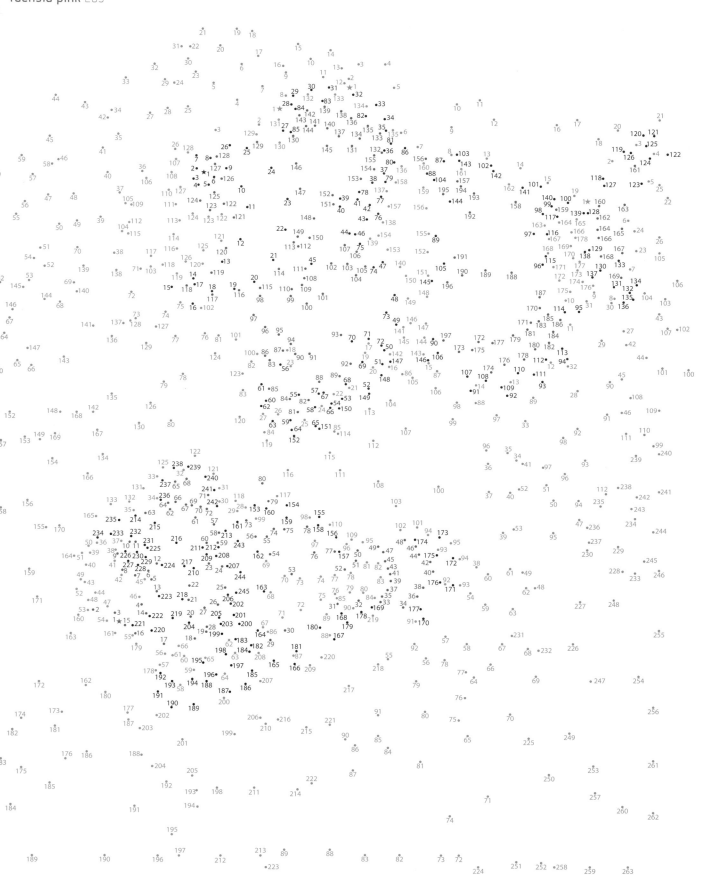

Scuttling Crabs

Scuttling Crabs

ORDER OF COLOUR SECTIONS

Face Off: Mandrill

Face Off: Mandrill

ORDER OF COLOUR SECTIONS

golden yellow 187   chocolate brown 179
bright blue 52   black 255
bright red 103

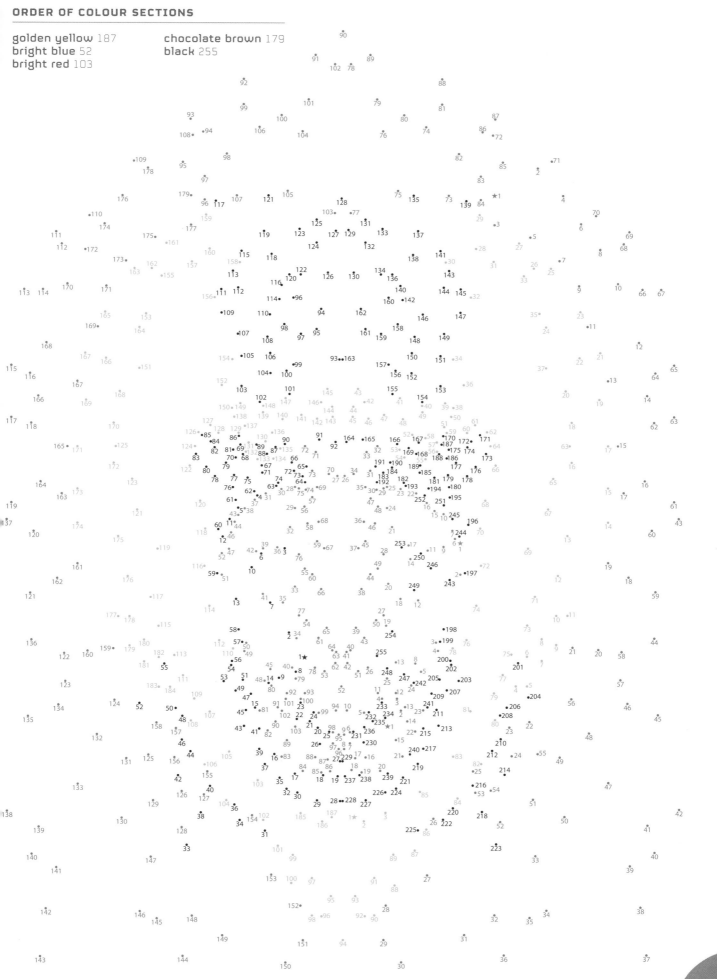

A Bloom of Jellyfish

ORDER OF COLOUR SECTIONS

sea blue 66
teal green 79
light orange 131

tangerine orange 198
dusty pink 188
purple pink 250

Regal Ram

ORDER OF COLOUR SECTIONS

orange 158   chocolate brown 381
soft grey 121   black 498
grass green 25

Hummingbird

ORDER OF COLOUR SECTIONS

green 127   fuchsia pink 64
royal blue 108   royal purple 192

Mandarin Duck

ORDER OF COLOUR SECTIONS

light orange 249
green 354
fuchsia pink 73

bright red 58
chocolate brown 37
indigo blue 173

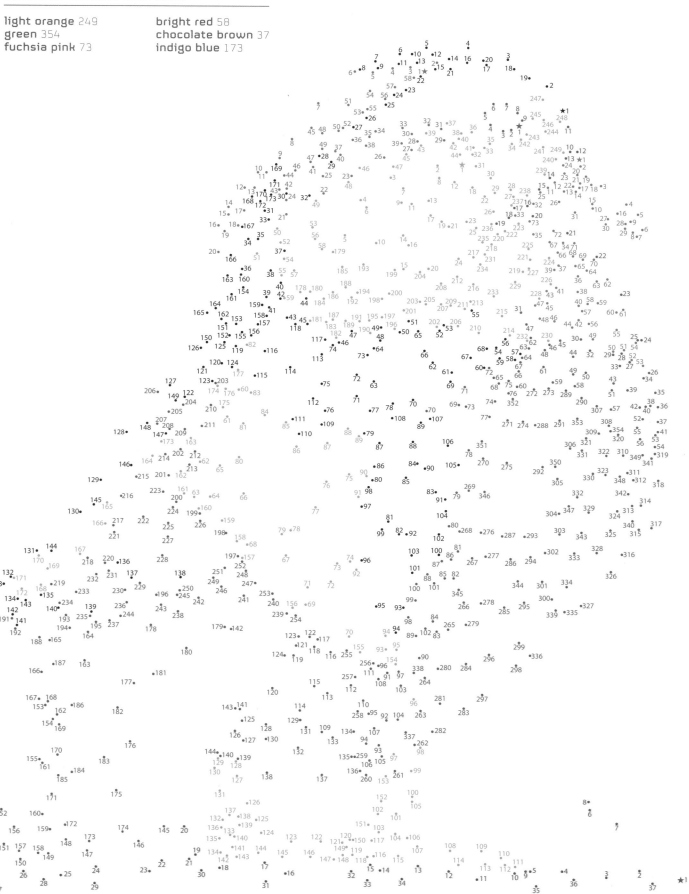

Prickly Hedgehog

ORDER OF COLOUR SECTIONS

pale grey 106	chestnut brown 58
leaf green 164	dark brown 219
dark green 49	black 42

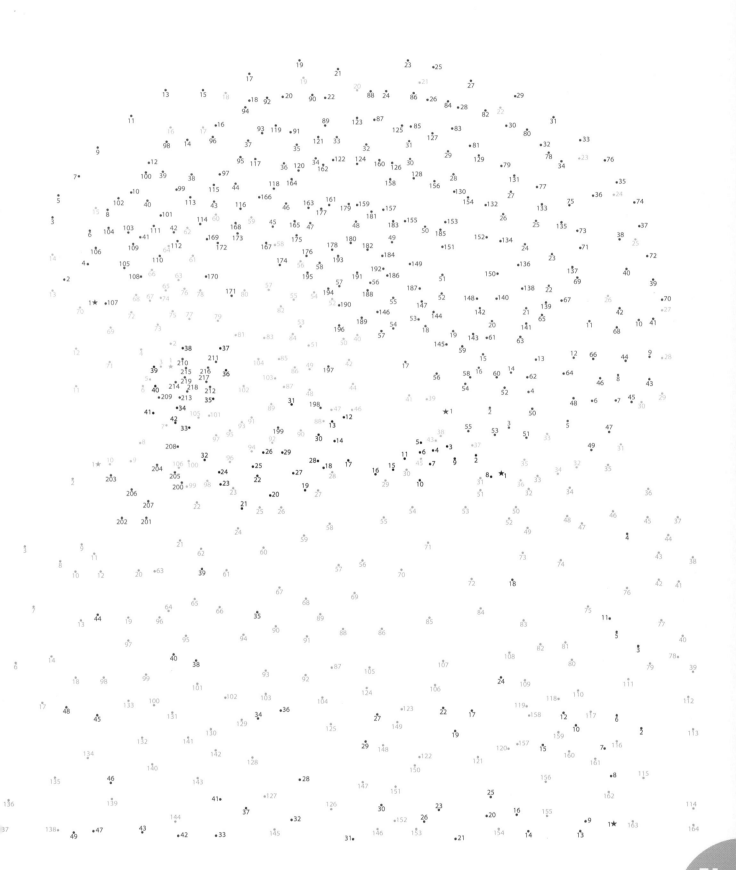

Colourful Bugs

ORDER OF COLOUR SECTIONS

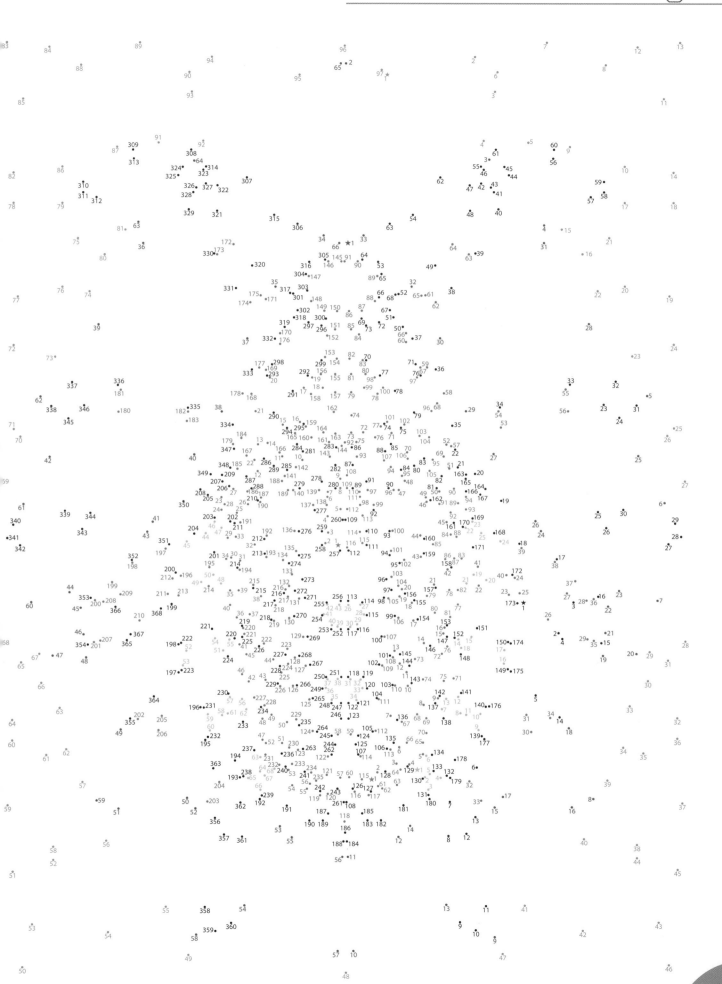

Majestic Horse

ORDER OF COLOUR SECTIONS

pale pink 96
caramel 398

chocolate brown 187
black 176

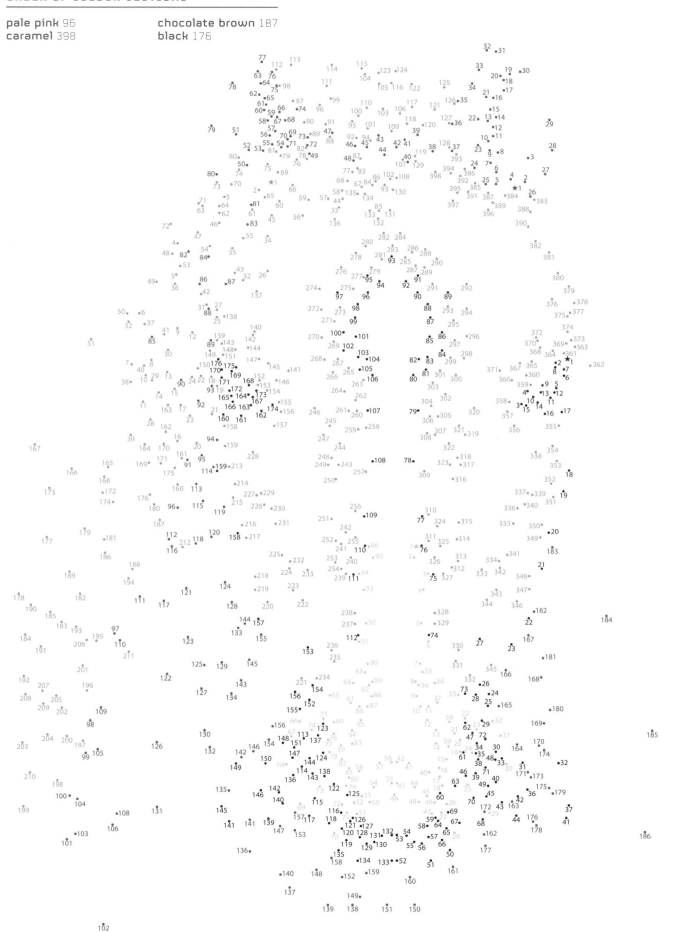

DOT-TO-DOT INDEX

Use the thumbnail images on the following pages to select the design you want to tackle next, or to help if you need any guidance when completing the puzzle.

Dawn Chorus
Page 17

Coral Reef Critters
Page 19

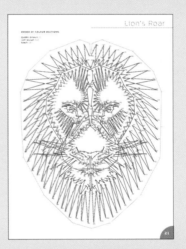

Lion's Roar
Page 21

Macaws
Page 23

Crowing Cockerel
Page 25

Flutter Butterfly
Page 27

Tiger Stripes
Page 29

Flamingo Duo
Page 31

Elegant Giraffes
Page 33

Slithering Snakes
Page 35

Cheeky Raccoon
Page 37

Proud Peacock
Page 39

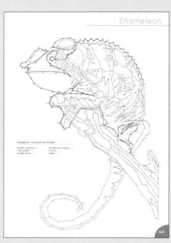

Dolphin Pod
Page 41

Chameleon
Page 43

The Fox
Page 45

Talk Toucan
Page 47

Frog Leap
Page 49

Chilled Turtle
Page 51

Vivid Gecko
Page 53

Delicate Dragonfly
Page 55

Clown Fish
Page 57

Scuttling Crabs
Page 59

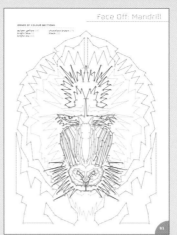

Face Off: Mandrill
Page 61

A Bloom of Jellyfish
Page 63

Regal Ram
Page 65

Hummingbird
Page 67

Mandarin Duck
Page 69

Prickly Hedgehog
Page 71

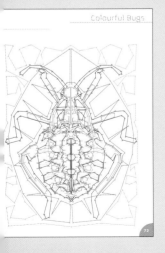

Colourful Bugs
Page 73

Majestic Horse
Page 75

DOT-TO-DOT INDEX

Acknowledgements

Quantum Books would like to thank the following for supplying images for inclusion in this book:

Shutterstock.com
Vichy Deal, page 9
Sonya illustration, page 13 (top left)
Pictures_for_You, page 13 (top centre and right)
NattapolStudiO, page 13 (lower right)

Thanks to the following for their help in making this book:

To our fantastic illustrator Shane Madden, thank you for bringing this concept to life and producing such wonderful artwork. It has been great fun creating this riot of colour with you.

To Emma Frith Suttey for her expert checking of all the puzzles and constant enthusiasm for the project.

Thanks also to Tilly Davis, Charlotte Frost, Emma Harverson, Nicky Hill, Tokiko Morishima and Julia Shone for their editorial work; and to Mike Lebihan for the design work and cover design.